Being Covid-19 Smart at School

NOT Sharing Is Caring!

Written By: B. Mater Cofield

Illustrated By: Kiana Setenza Henderson

Edited By: Eunice Portillo

Audio Book Narrated By: B. Mater Cofield

Audiobook recorded and engineered by: Kevin Cooper

INTRODUCTION

This book was written for elementary school students, the dedicated and courageous educators that teach them, as well as staff and administrators many who are either entering school for the first time or returning to classrooms in the fall of 2020, in the midst of the global Covid-19 Coronavirus pandemic. Together we can stop the spread!

Not Sharing Is Caring

2nd Edition

Copyright © 2019 B. Mater Cofield

Audiobook mastered by Soufroud

Layout and typesetting: Hatice Bayramoglu

Illustrations: Kiana Setenza Henderson

"Sharing Is Caring," that's what we've been told, but
NOT Sharing Is Caring, I know that sounds cold.

We care for our friends and our hearts are the same.
To keep yourselves safe though, some things must change.

There are many ways to show that we care for our friends,
but sharing's not one of them until Covid-19 ends.

So friends, when you're in school...

Do not share your pencils, erasers, or crayons,
it's not a good idea because sharing spreads germs.

Don't share your water bottles, juice boxes, or milk.
Get your own drinks please so no one gets sick.

Do not share your fruit, Hot Cheetos, or lunch.
Remember to bring your own goodies to munch.

4

Don't share your jackets, your hoodies, or gloves.
Just say, "no thank you," but say it with love.

Never share your tissue, your napkins, or mask.
Whisper, "please ask the teacher," and get back on task.

Don't share your Pokémon cards or your toys.
You can't share with girls and you can't share with boys.

You can't share your ruler, your scissors, or glue.
Sharing supplies can spread the coronavirus flu.

8

No need to share perfume, lip gloss, or lotion.
Follow directions, it's for your own protection.

Never pick up band-aids from off the floor.
Do not apply band-aids on friends anymore.

Please don't share Chromebooks, tablets, or phones.
Say, "I'm using these items, please use your own."

No more sharing spoons, forks, or straws.
It's not even safe if you first wash them off.

Please don't share paper, folders, or books.
Remember there's only one backpack per hook.

No need to share scrunchies, a comb, or a brush.
Pull your hair back and don't make a fuss.

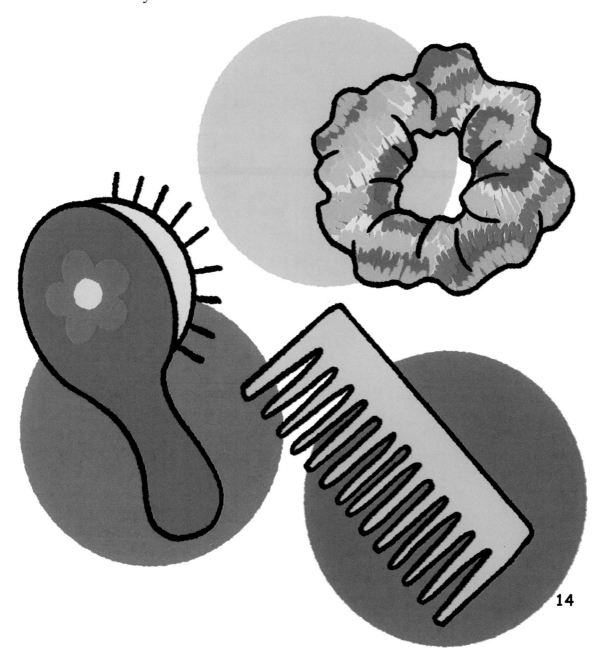

14

Only one friend per seat, stool, or chair.
Keep a safe distance and show that you care.

15

Don't share your recorder, violin, or your flute.
Stay 6 feet apart when you play as a group.

Keep track of your paintbrush, color pencils and clay.
When you're done, wipe them down and tuck them away.

For all of you ballers who love to play ball…
no close contact, no defense,
get some shots in, that's all!

Last year you probably played tag with your friends.
Well, no more tag until Covid-19 ends.

19

No more high fives, no more holding hands,
and make sure you line up 6 feet from your friends.

Keep a safe distance of 6 feet apart.
I know you can do it! You're super-duper smart!

Covid has changed how we behave at school.
We'll be just fine though... if we follow safety rules.

Some friends might get sad or say you're not nice,
just remind them it's not safe sharing school supplies.

You are not being selfish, it's not SAFE to share.
Your safety comes first, it's important! BEWARE!

24

Just hold your head high and do the right thing.
Not sharing dear friends is your brand-new routine.
A routine is something we practice each day.
NOT Sharing Is Caring and keeps everyone safe.

So you see friends …

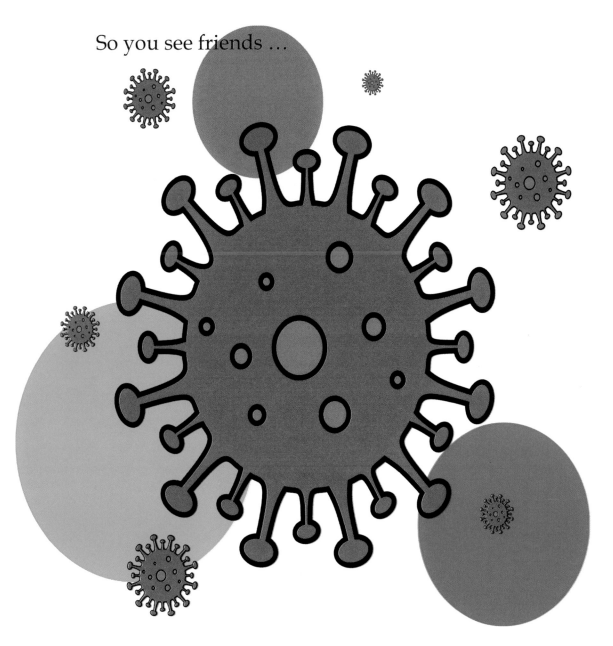

To share is to care, is a thing of the past.
Sharing spreads germs INCREDIBLY fast!   26

You can show that you care when you smile with your eyes.
You could draw a nice picture and hold it up high.

Heart hands are nice, you can put them up fast.
Care for your friends, you can still have a blast!

But remember...
Social distance, wash your hands and PLEASE,
Pretty please, PLEASE wear your mask!

Made in the USA
Middletown, DE
13 May 2021